If thou art borrowed
by a friend,
Right welcome
shall he be,
To read, to study,
not to lend,
But to return to me.

THIS BOOK BELONGS TO
PHYLLIS GRISWOLD

If thou art borrowed
by a friend,
Right welcome
shall he be,
To read, to study,
not to lend,
But to return to me.

THIS BOOK BELONGS TO
6564 FOUNTAIN AVE
HOLLYWOOD, CALIFORNIA

LETTERS TO SUSAN

July 18, 1941

Phyllis — in gratitude that
you are as you are.

Mother.

Letters to Susan

* * * * * * * * * * * * * *

By

Margaret Culkin Banning

* * * * * * * * * * * * * *

HARPER & BROTHERS PUBLISHERS

NEW YORK   1936   LONDON

CONTENTS

[v]

Contents

THE SITUATION

The Situation

WE EXPECT so much. Out of our in-
adequacies, our frustrations, our hopes,
and our affections, we adults build up towers
of demands upon the young. I sometimes think
the towers are higher for girls than for boys.
Every new achievement of women, every new
responsibility assumed by them gives us a
new ambition for the young girl and sug-
gests further preparation. We are continually
adding to what we think she should know,
hardly ever subtracting.

When my daughter was seventeen years
old I added up the demands that I was making
upon her and set them down in the order that
they occurred to me, as they are listed here.

[3]

I found, to my surprise, that I expected her to be able to do all these varied things:

Pass examinations in Chemistry, French, Latin and Mathematics.

Decide on her preferences among further studies with a view to concentration of effort and to ultimately earning her living.

Meet strangers pleasantly.

Handle her own personal expenses on a small allowance and not ask me for additional money.

Play golf and tennis, one in the competition of a tournament.

Dance well.

Face stag lines at parties.

Read intelligently. Nor did I want her reading to be trivial or merely an occupation to pass the time. I expected her to be familiar with "The Imitation of Christ," Emily Dickinson's Poems, and other classics. It did not

[4]

seem to me that she was too young to read some of the works of the modern writers, of Ernest Hemingway, Virginia Woolf, Kay Boyle or William Faulkner.

Order food for simple but formal meals, as well as to provide plenty of provisions for the irregular hospitality of a country cottage, and keep the marketing bills down to a stipulated amount for each month of the summer.

Select many of her own clothes and have suitable ones ready for all her sports and activities. Keep these clothes reasonably clean and fresh.

Refrain from drinking without being priggish.

Prevent boys who "took her out" from indulging in necking.

Write necessary letters of courtesy as well as the letters she wanted to write.

Leave the kitchen and living-rooms in order

after impromptu entertaining at night, no matter how late it happened to be.

Be agreeable to her relatives and to those family friends in whom she had no interest.

Drive a car without accidents, wash it, change a tire if necessary.

Swim.

Ride horseback.

Keep some of her day for herself.

I was slightly ashamed of that list after I had made it, because there were so many things on it that I myself could not do. Nor was she the measure of perfection, as a crumpled fender, an irritated aunt, and an often empty purse showed. Nevertheless, this is what I desired in the way of accomplishment from my daughter. These attainments and facilities and habits were those which I wanted her to have. I did not want to cross anything off that list, long as it was, and in the subsequent few years I have lengthened it. Total abstinence from alcohol has been changed to the more difficult requirement of temperance. Reading and studying have become more involved and profound.

It may seem confused and incoherent, if not pointless, this array of domestic, athletic, financial, social and intellectual accomplishments. Why should a girl know so much? Why do I want her equipped to face the cold horror of a modern ballroom as well as to enter an office or classroom or laboratory? Why do I want her to know how to clean a kitchen as well as to be able to translate Latin?

The answer is that I believe it is necessary. Her equipment must be diversified because I do not know what her future will be. Her future set-up is not as clear as that of a young man, because a woman's destiny today is being altered by her changing relationships to the world. I do not want her stultified or cramped by my notions of independent womanhood, for I suspect that the future independence of women will be more generous and more companionable than it was in its inception and in its early stages. A girl today should certainly be prepared to earn her own living, but at the same time she should be prepared to manage her life successfully if someone else earns it for her. She may be a mother or a spinster, a scientist or a society woman and she will want to do a good job in any case. Whether she works in an office or lives a life of amusement, she must be familiar with some forms of exercise. And as I believe that some domestic responsibility, feather-weight or back-breaking, will ultimately and surely become her personal problem, she should know how to handle that when it comes.

It is easy for a parent to be presumptuous

in assuming the future of his child. I have two friends whose main business in life is bringing up their daughters. One is rich and a widower. One is a divorced woman who, successfully enough, earns her own living but is not wealthy. Their points of view are divergent and yet their ideals are so identical that they fascinate me. For both of these parents want their girls to be well-educated, aristocratic in the bravest sense, competent and happy. They chose the schools for the girls with the greatest care and, curiously enough, they chose the same schools. But outside of the schools they shape them absolutely differently. The woman wants her daughters to be free from dependence on any man, and so able to stand alone that she has almost isolated them among her own ideals. The man, who can not conceive of not having his daughters marry, is insistent that they develop every

[9]

grace. He promotes their social popularity. Both the man and woman have said to me on separate occasions when I have brought the conversation to the point of considering social upheaval, "Whatever happens, my girls would be adequate. They could meet any situation." But it is true that all four of the girls are self-conscious and unhappy at times. I have never seen girls suffer so much at a mixed houseparty as that woman's daughters, and the man's daughters are completely at a loss if they fall into a company in which the conversation is so intellectual that it forgets certain graces and courtesies. If, by any chance, the lives of these girls develop differently from what their parents so firmly expect, they will doubtless be self-conscious all through their lives.

Until a girl's emotions reach fulfillment or are permanently channeled into the pursuit of some major interest, her life is a gamble. This is far more true of girls than boys and it is why I think a girl often needs to know things that exceed or even contradict a parent's ambitions for her or a girl's ambition for herself.

From the essential things, one honestly tries to separate prejudices or favoritisms. For example, I do not think that every girl should know how to ride. Plenty of girls are afraid of horses and can not overcome the fear, and plenty of them can't afford the sport. Nor is Latin an essential knowledge. There are a few things on the list of accomplishments I wanted for my own daughter that are no more than reflections of special aptitudes discovered in her or reflected desires of my own. But one can quickly weed them out and essential things are still indicated.

· · · · ·

Before going any further one must take into account the vast diversity of education. How much can a girl learn under ordinary circumstances or under the best circumstances? What is offered in this country to girls between twelve and twenty in the way of education and training? It is a long range. There are those astonishing schools where a "good seat in the saddle" will almost insure a diploma; there are serious and gratifying boarding schools; there are others that in their feeble way try to maintain class distinctions in the minds of young girls on the payment of large fees. Most inclusive of all there are the High Schools. For continuing education, the possibilities for a girl are not very different from what they are for a young man, divided between a number of women's colleges, a few convents which are now fairly secularized in curriculum at least, and many co-educational universities.

Nearly every girl, even in the horsey schools, will be taught to read and write and cipher. In the best schools she will learn to study and become aware that the mind is a fine instrument of use and pleasure. She will be given information about Macbeth, Walter Pater, geometry, musical history and other unallied subjects. If she goes to college, this knowledge will probably—not always, by any means—be importantly increased. In a girls' school or college she will also learn the problems and failures and satisfactions of Utopias for women. In a High School or co-educational university she will, as a rule, learn enough facts to keep her there from year to year, and she will also learn far too much about American snobbery. For the High Schools, though I may be doubted on this, have an almost perfect system of social classification and recognition.

On the whole I should say that most of what

[13]

a girl learns in her classes at school, wherever she may be taught, will fade very quickly. The reading and writing, a trifle of geography and a fragment of history will perhaps remain. She will remember names like Longfellow and Emerson. But little factual knowledge will stick to her mind if she has the general education of most girls, unless she goes on studying past the point at which most girls stop.

I am not quite willing to pass this point without criticism. For I believe that a girl should know how to think, how to concentrate, and we have a right to expect that the academic side of her life, the schooling proper, will teach her this. If schools were devoted more to learning than to society, exercise and new buildings, I think it could be done even in a limited education and surely in a generous one. However, I am grateful even for the reading and writing and arithmetic. It is a start anyway. From there we can go on.

What I want to enumerate (and try to elucidate) are those other kinds of knowledge and additional skills which a girl should accumulate while her future is hanging in the balance. Like my own daughter, she may intend to study science, but she may be deflected from that purpose when she begins to study economics or meets a man from Harvard. I do not want, because she has a special interest now, either to neglect it or let it color her life to such an extent that she will be unhappy or inadequate if her desires change and her habits of life turn out to be quite different from those I imagine for her or she dreams for herself. I want her to know the things that will stand her in good stead if she is poor; or if she is rich; if the state is Communist or Republican; if she has a happy marriage, is divorced or remains single; if she should marry a man stationed in China or in an army post; if she builds herself a cottage in Carolina or has a job in a bank in New York.

It must, then, be knowledge which is not too largely dependent on locality. In other words, though we live in the North and are surrounded by hills, I do not want her to be a skiing expert and nothing else. Nor, on the other hand, do I want her to be one of those "well-rounded" people who are much too round to have real direction or passionate purpose in their lives.

I know only one way to approach the problem. It is true that I can not foretell what her individual life will be, but I know what a woman's life in the world involves today and what obligations women as a sex have assumed for tomorrow. For those I can, to some extent, prepare her, because I can see into what divisions her duties must inevitably fall. She will have a business life of some sort, even if it is limited to paying her bills or shopping on credit. She will have a domestic life almost certainly, for domestic life persists even in strange new forms. She will have many social dealings with men and women. She will have personal relations with herself. For these four things I want, by hook or crook, by play or work, to fit her; and when I say "her" now, I do not mean only my own daughter but the daughters of my friends and of strangers, and the multitudes of girls who will be graduated from schools this year. All of these four things they must face. Into these four channels of life we must direct a girl's knowledge and her skill.

. . . . .

When I say business dealings I do not mean a job. I think a girl should know how to earn her living, of course. She can no longer count on an income from any other source. When I think of all the women who thought five years ago that they were "fixed for life" and now are in a desperate way trying to sell lingerie or cosmestics, I hardly think this point needs proof. For everyone knows as many of these unfortunate and usually unskilled women as I do. A girl who can not earn her living may be arrogantly set apart by her unearned income (and that, as I say, is terribly precarious today), but she is usually an adventurer, living by her wits and the practice of her emotions or by setting up claims to devotion. I do not care how happily married she may be. She would be even more happily married if she knew that she could earn her living.

It often is not necessary for her to do it, at least continually. But any girl I bring up is going to know the delightful feeling of an earned dollar. The sense of earning, the personal confidence it gives a girl, the awareness that her energy or ability has a market value, is immeasurably valuable. That knowledge keeps a girl from all sorts of secret discontents and fears. If she marries it is apt to make her relations with her husband truer and freer, because, while she may quite properly be living on his income, she isn't in terror lest he lose it or tire of her. The ability of a woman to earn money has made some difficult married situations no doubt, but it has destroyed so much hypocrisy and humiliation that there is no question that it is one of the most important things a girl should know. Also, a girl should know how to earn money so that she may realize the value of a dollar. Very extravagant and very stingy women are usually those who do not know how to earn a nickel.

When my daughter finishes her schooling she will, I think, have found a way to earn her living. But if she has not, and it is not discreditable for a girl to be undirected professionally even at twenty-one or -two, I shall send her to a business college for a few months and then expect her to find a job. Any job, just as a boy would have to do. I would not let her stumble around, among parties and households, until she is thirty and then discover that her education had gone stale and that she had no method of earning except badgering her friends to buy trinkets or luxuries out of friendship.

Yet to be fair, it must be admitted that it isn't always possible for every girl to know how to earn money. She may marry very young, sometimes advisedly. But even then she will have business dealings with the world. She will shop. She will market. She will be responsible for spending money. And this responsibility should be handled adequately. That is why, when my daughter, on the twenty-eighth of July, has thirteen cents and no gasoline in her Ford, she has to get along as best she can until the first of August, afoot. That is why I have her do the marketing and give her only a certain amount to spend. That is why she is told that she can have a new evening dress if she can find one for less than twenty dollars.

The world has been full to the brim with charming, dishonest women who have had a whole lot to do with steering it on the rocks. They can be just as charming if they are honest; and that they cheat is not exclusively their fault, for husbands, fathers and shopkeepers have winked in an amused or surly way at the notion that women always spend more than they should, and in some twisted way linked this failing up to a tribute to man's guardianship and superiority.

That is very tiresome. It is also old stuff. A girl should know how to write a check—and when I say check I include an entry on a check stub. The ciphering in public schools often helps us out on this point by including the writing of checks in common arithmetic. A girl should know that a bank account is not a bottomless pit. But if she has no bank account, she can at least know how much cash or what portion of her parents' or husband's credit she can spend.

She should know, and at a reasonably early age, something about insurance and investments. This does not have to be expert knowledge, but it should be a knowledge definitely and closely related to her income and responsibilities. I know young teachers who almost pride themselves on "never having a cent." For some reason they consider it spirited. But it shows that in spite of being educators themselves, they lack one of the forms of knowledge every girl should have, that of proper business dealings with the world.

It gets down to this. A girl should know how to handle what money she has, whether it is five dollars or a half million. The sight of a girl who is putting herself through school by waiting on table gives me a complete confidence as to that girl's ability to keep out of bankruptcy all her life. But the girl who says, "I couldn't possibly afford it! But it was so adorable that I just had to have it," has not been taught how to spend. And she will be saying the same thing all the rest of her life, unless a new social order chokes the words in her throat.

· · · · ·

It seems to me beyond question that a girl should know something about domestic life and household management. Here I run wild with preferences. For I would rather have a girl know how to clean a sink (or a bath tub) than make a lemon pie. I prefer knowledge of cleanliness to knowledge of cookery, and accomplishment in neatness to fine sewing.

Personally I think cooking is one of the most satisfactory things in the world because it is so tangible an accomplishment. But though we make hundreds of glasses of jelly in my own house every summer, I have not thought it necessary for my daughter to know how to make jelly.

I have insisted that she know how many pounds of peas to buy for six people and at what season to buy melons and avoid grapes, as well as the difference between shoulder, rib and loin lamb chops, and a standing or rolled roast of beef. I want her to know how to make good coffee, good tea, broil a chop or a steak, make a salad and put a meal on the table without getting breathless. I want her to know how to get breakfast. Beyond that I would leave further knowledge about cookery to the pressure and temptation of her future circumstances. Who knows what cookery will be necessary in the future?

I believe that a girl should know how to take a temperature and care for a minor illness or accident. She should know how to make a bed. Few do. I think she should know that there is no peace of mind in a confused or disorderly room. She should know how to arrange flowers and make something charming out of six miserable calendulas if necessary.

But, lest you imagine that I think her household talents should be administrative or decorative only, let me add at once that she should know how to wash clothes, and iron clothes. But I do not think she needs to know how to make darning look like fine tapestry.

These things are all relevant to my own conviction that a household's grace and much of its happiness are dependent on order and cleanliness and beauty. Even if a girl lives in a cabin on a boat or in a service flat, many of these aptitudes will be useful. If she has a normal household they will be basic.

There is one other thing about domestic life that it is necessary for a girl to know; and that is how to get along well with her family. In every family this effort has to start somewhere, and men and boys succumb most easily to business moods, or bad golf scores, or boils. A girl should know how to appear cheerful when she is not cheerful, and look serene at the table when she is troubled. It is part of her woman's job.

One always feels, at intervals, that girls should know more about the care of infants and children than most of them do. But this is usually panic. It has always seemed to me that any artificial attempt to stimulate a love of babies in young girls was bound to fail. It is one of the things which we can leave to nature, and we are doing so much of nature's work for her now that she ought to be willing to keep on at that one job. The most ignorant or most frivolous girl, when she is brought up against the problems of motherhood and must take on the care of a child, learns with marvelous quickness and retention—if she wants to. Every fine quality in a girl pours into her first experience in motherhood, and there is time enough for learning detailed knowledge

[27]

during pregnancy and hospitalization. Before that, it seems to me that if a girl knows that a household is normally made up of people of different ages, if she is affectionate with her grandparents and pleasant to a three-year-old visiting niece, she has the fundamental idea.

.   .   .   .   .

Domestic life weaves into social life and sometimes the fabrics blend. But social relations, especially those with boys and men, are so important that a girl should have special knowledge about them to guide her. I make no exceptions. Every young girl is involved. She may escape business dealings almost entirely, she may touch domestic life only with the tips of her fingers, but she is sure to have social relations that will bring her pain and happiness. And while she is a girl she will give a major part of her imaginings, her hopes and her intentions to the relations between herself and men. This is true, no matter how she is brought up.

Some parents and guardians have a scorn for such absorption and treat it as if it were of no account, or a little comical. And there is an academic school of thought which considers it as an old-fashioned preoccupation sloughed off entirely by the modern girl. This is not true. The normal modern girl, without abandoning the victories of feminism, and accepting its responsibilities, does not even want to imagine a life in which men play no part. Therefore she should be fortified by accomplishment and equipment for such relations.

One begins with those general social relations which lead to closer ones between individuals, and for these a knowledge of how to dress, how to play games, how to dance, how to talk well, and conduct oneself in company are the major points. It is very necessary for a girl to know how to wear her clothes to advantage and make the most of herself physically. This includes what beauty parlor experts would doubtless call the discovery of her own personality as expressed by her appearance. When a girl is sure of that, she will know such minor things as whether to use a dark shade of powder or wear a white bathing-suit. She should know, too, that it is not necessary to be beautiful in order to be charming. She should know that no well-dressed person thinks about her looks all the time.

She must know how to use her voice. The shrill clatter of some girls' voices definitely destroys their charm. I do not mean to suggest affectation or the grafting of accents which are unsuitable and out of place. But a girl should speak so that it is pleasant to listen to her. If this were universally true, fewer homes would break up. If a girl is surrounded by

[30]

people with raucous voices, she can always go to the talkies and listen to one of the few actresses who speak beautifully, and learn from them how musical the English language can be.

She must know how to dance. Dancing is essential and it is the great leveller. There are dances for five cents a whirl and dances to which only several thousand dollars a season will give admittance, but at all of them are the same competitions and sufferings and successes. Uncounted parents have tried to find a solution for the cruelty of the modern dances, and there doesn't seem to be any answer except that a girl should know how to dance very well. Otherwise, a girl shouldn't be exposed to a dance where mercy is left in the cloak-rooms. She should know, if her parents do not, that it is better to stay at home than be pilloried.

But dancing is not enough. A girl must

[31]

know other sports. She should swim. This, like dancing, is within the reach of every purse, for we have public beaches as well as public dance halls. She should know how to swim for safety and for pleasure. But after reaching this point I would let a girl choose her further sports. In my own family we have been pretty catholic and had even our archery and fencing attempts—these at camp and school. They petered out and left the more conventional, widely shared sports.

A girl who knows how to drive a golf ball a decent distance or return a serve well in tennis, or ride a horse without wondering if he is going to throw her, has a resource, a means of healthy development and an opportunity to meet men in their sports.

I think a girl should know how to do one such thing quite well. If it is golf, let it be golf. If it is riding, let it be that. These are no longer merely the privileges of the rich. Public tennis courts and golf courses are everywhere. But to know one sport to a high point of excellence seems to me far better than to have a smattering of all of them. This applies particularly to one indoor sport, bridge. I am not at all sure that girls should be allowed to play bridge unless they really know the game. This country is too crowded with women who sort cards and can do little else except tell one suit from another and make mistakes, whose minds are cluttered by rules that they can't follow. I do not care personally whether a girl ever touches a card or not. But if she plays bridge I think she should know the game.

One is not always engaged in sports, so there must be supplementary knowledge of general conduct. My first principle is that a girl should know how to keep herself from

being what is called "necked." I know I shall
be criticized when I say that I think that some
of this adolescent or post-adolescent caressing
that goes on does little harm. I have seen a
boy kiss a girl at the end of a dance and it was
no more than a graceful gesture. They liked
each other. I couldn't see any great harm in
it. Anyway, we can think what we please but
the caresses go on. However, for necking as
a deliberate indulgence I have no tolerance
at all. It is utterly bad, because it excites both
girls and boys past the point proper for their
ages and habits, and because it gradually de-
bauches a girl who can only hope that her
husband will be as successful a necker as others
she has known. There is no distinction, you
may say? Well, ask some frank girl to tell
you if she doesn't know every necker in her
crowd.

I feel equally strongly about excessive
drinking. I know of no valid reason why a

girl should drink. It will do her no physical good. It will steadily decrease her ability to have a good time without a drink. She should know how not to drink, without making a fuss about it or calling attention to herself; and if, at a proper age, she takes a cocktail or a glass of wine, she should know how to refuse another.

These are strange times and unsteady ones and so she should have one knowledge that will perhaps not be as necessary for another generation. That is how to treat drunken boys and men, for she is almost bound to see some of them. This is not the age of drawing the skirt aside. It is the age of tolerance. It is suitable here to mention also that a girl should know how to control gossip and protect a good name. She should know how to be amusing but to avoid coarseness. She ought to know how to head off a bad story.

It comes in aptly here to add that a girl

should know how to drive a car. Often a modern girl has to know how to drive a car for safety alone. She should be able to handle any make of car, know how to drive without showing off or posing in the middle of traffic. I said in the beginning that I wanted my daughter to know how to wash a car and change a tire. That is partly in the interests of economy and partly because those things cement the affection of ownership.

The last necessary knowledge in this matter of social relations is that a girl should know the difference between passion and love. Someone will say that this knowledge only comes by experience, and that, to some extent, is true. But its basis is clear sex knowledge, which of course can not be neglected. Girls find out much for themselves and among themselves, but their knowledge should be checked up on its accuracy by those adults who

[36]

love them. There is such a thing as intimate discussion, as the pointing out of illustrative cases, and there are books and movies and theaters and physical attractions which prove that passion is not love and rarely becomes it.

. . . . .

But there are other things she must know, in addition to all these. For men are going to disappoint her, sometimes at the best, always at the worst. Jobs and work can go terribly stale. Her domestic life is bound to be interrupted and terrified by illness and calamity sooner or later. Is she to have no preparation against such things?

I think she should have it and can have it. In the first place, she should know how to read. I mean that she should know to transfer the contents of a printed page to her mind, not just skim over a few columns of movie gossip. She should be able to get something to rest and stimulate her out of imaginative literature and critical literature. If possible, she should know how to play the piano, for if you are in trouble your radio may drive you mad, but your piano will be your comfort.

She must know how to be alone. Much of an average woman's life has lonely stretches in it which will frighten her if she has not learned as a girl the pleasure of being alone. If she has to run to a woman's club or to the telephone to keep herself from solitude, she lacks proper resource. She does not really destroy or use her solitude that way. So I think a girl should be taught that it is a pleasure to be alone, to have time for a solitary walk, for thought, and for figuring out what every human being has to do before he is through, whether he is glad he was born and why. She should know something about the woods besides the fact that they are green in summer.

She should know how to pray. There come times in the life of every woman which are hard and unsheltered by human comfort, and prayer is then as natural as necessary. It is the cry against a purposeless life. The girl who is most fortunate will have a sustaining faith and religion. But many have nothing of the sort nowadays. Everything that can be done to give them a philosophy sufficient to life should be done, for they will need it sooner or later.

. . . . .

If I am demanding, it is because I care so much. I know what a great burden is on the girl of today, and for all her apparent nonchalance, she knows it too. She must carry all the new responsibilities we can conjure up for her, earn her living and somehow re-

[39]

store and improve much of the charm that harsher feminists tossed aside. She must be able to earn her way, pay her own fare, and yet have every quality of feminine companionship. She must meet the terrible competition of emotion in the world today, which is worse than it ever was because of the early start it gets and the prolongation it insists on among both men and women.

If we had a safe, settled adult world to open to a girl, if we could promise her even a choice between a small job and a good man's love, it would be different. But we are so confused ourselves that we can not distinguish between the basic and the temporary. We only know this: that little of the danger and happiness that girls ever faced has been destroyed, and more peril and fortunately more joy have been added.

THE LETTERS

I

MUST WE HAVE CHAPERONS?

I

November 15, 1934

DEAR SUSAN: No, you can't drive to Detroit for Thanksgiving with the two boys and Ann. I thought that I'd better put that simple, declarative sentence at the beginning of this letter so that you wouldn't be kept in suspense even if you are put in a bad temper. I'm sorry to have to be so definite and final. I would like to leave the decision to your own judgment, but this is one of the few times when I can't do that. For the judgment of so many people, young and old, is a little askew about just such propositions as four young people motoring together for most of two days and a night without any stops except for breath and coffee.

I do agree with much of what you wrote me. It would be delightful to be there for that Thanksgiving dance and it wouldn't be expensive to carry out your plan. I quite understand that you can manage the complicated schedules all around by leaving Wednesday afternoon, driving all that night and most of Thursday, and I don't doubt that you would have a grand time until Saturday noon and all be back in college by Sunday night. Also I know that Mark is probably the best driver of all your friends and that he behaves well. His father was like that too. He was also—though this bit of history may not interest you—rather dashing in his ways, like Mark. I don't know the other boy, David, or is it Daniel? (your handwriting certainly doesn't get any better) but I'll take your word for all the sterling qualities you say he has. Nobody need argue with me about Ann, after the way she measured up to family troubles and kept gay all last summer. Even you are all that I sometimes say you are, but it doesn't affect the situation.

In fact, I think it aggravates it. Such young people as you four have no right to do things that confuse you with people who are quite different in habits and ideas of control. You write, quote, please don't say that I can't go because of the looks of the thing because that's such rubbish and not like you, unquote. You're wrong on both counts. It is not rubbish and it is like me. I get a little angry about this high-handed scrapping of the looks of things. What else have we to go by? How else can the average person form an opinion of a girl's sense of values or even of her chastity except by the looks of her conduct? If looks are so unimportant, why do you yourself spend so much time on your physical looks before you go out with strangers? In your own crowd you will go around all day wearing shorts and a sweat shirt and that eternal and dreadful red checked scarf that should be burned. But if you are going to be with people you don't know or who don't know who you are, it is different. Then you are careful to make yourself look as if you were decently bred, as if you could read and write, and as if you had good taste in clothes and cosmetics. You wouldn't be caught wearing cheap perfume, would you? Then why do you want to wear cheap perfume on your conduct?

Looks do matter and I do not mean just hair and skin and teeth and clothes. Looks are also your social contact with the world. Suppose you take this drive. How would it look to strangers? Two young men (of marriageable

[46]

age) take two young women (also of marriageable age) on a forty-hour drive. Everyone knows that many girls go on forty-hour drives with men with extremely bad results, such as over-excited emotions, reckless conduct, and road accidents. How is anyone to make a special case of you? Why should anyone? It looks as if you deliberately assumed the pathetic privileges of girls who want to be with men at any cost to their reputations.

You wrote also that you think that it is nobody's business except your own what you do, but you are wrong. This is the kind of world—and there doesn't seem to be any other—in which conduct is social as well as individual. The main point of your education, from kindergarten up, has been to make you understand that, and I don't want you to break down at this small test. Your conduct is not entirely your own business, though it begins there. Afterwards it affects other people's conduct. Other girls, seeing you go off on an unchaperoned motor jaunt, think it's all right to do the same thing. Parents doubt and wonder. Men, and even boys, grow skeptical and more careless. You confuse things by such conduct.

I must also point out, even in the face of your cool young rage, that you ask a great deal more than gasoline and company of Mark and David—who may be Daniel. An unchaperoned girl, for whom a young man is responsible to parents whom he knows and respects, is a great burden to a young man. You are—so you said yourself—decent. Mark would have you on his hands in situations when people would not know whether you are decent or not. Suppose you all had an accident. Suppose, for example, that you couldn't make this trip without a long stop, speed being so eminently respectable but stops always so questionable. If you trail into some hotel after midnight, though a tourist camp should be all any of you can afford this year, it wouldn't be so easy for either of those boys. Did it ever occur to you that there's something almost crooked in the way decent girls nowadays use the shelter of their established respectability to make things awkward for men?

There's another thing in my mind which is only partly relevant. You make no mention of it, assuming the coolest of friendly relations between the four of you. But suppose that David-Daniel (I'm beginning to love that name) found himself more excited than you anticipate by the proximity—and what proximity!—of you two good-looking girls. That happens. I seem to remember having mentioned it before. It might happen to one of those two boys. And how about you and

[49]

Ann? Are you quite frank with me or yourselves? Isn't part of the lure of this trip the fact that you yourself do like Mark very much? Your plan really is to drive a car full of high explosives for forty hours, from dark to dawn, and enjoy your own daring no matter who blows up.

You wrote me that it would be such fun that you hope I'll see it your way. That's always a very disarming argument, but I think it's on my side this time. You see, if there were any necessity for this trip I would feel differently about it. If you were compelled for some real reason to travel that way, if there were a war or a siege to make it necessary, or if it were the only way you could see Mark for years, I would say that you could do it. But fun—that so-transient fun—of just missing being hit by a bus or finding the best hamburgers in the world at a roadside inn, or being cut in on twenty times at that Thanksgiving dance—isn't a good enough reason.

It is no fun for me either, to disappoint you like this. It isn't easy to be the person who sometimes has to try to preserve your happiness at the expense of your fun. After Thanksgiving—I know you probably can't do it until then—will you please believe that's true?

With love to you, Ann, Mark and David-Daniel,

MOTHER

II

THE UNPOPULAR GIRL

II

December 14, 1934

DEAR SUSAN: I'm so glad that you are
going to get here on the twenty-third
and that you are bringing Ruth Beckwith
home with you. Of course I remember meeting
her that day when you and your friends had
lunch with me in New York. She was the
one with the blue knitted suit. I'm sure she
was, for I remember the talk centered on what
other clothes she should buy and the rest of
you were giving her advice out of an evidently
inexhaustible store as to what would be becoming, startling and alluring. I remember
thinking at the time that she would be a very

[53]

unusual and possibly beautiful woman if she didn't take too many of those helpful hints. It's going to be very pleasant to have her in the house. I hope she likes her Christmas trees trimmed in silver and white, and her turkey dressing with plenty of onion and sage.

We certainly must see that she has a good time. I understand why you are worrying a little about that, much as you admire and like her, and why it troubles you that Ruth isn't the kind of girl who is easily and quickly popular with boys, and says she's afraid of parties. I wish we hadn't allowed parties, especially dances, to become such a strain. Until these last years the girl whose popularity was only grade B had a much greater chance to enjoy herself, or at least to be unnoticed even if she was unhappy, than she has now. Even the wallflower was more comfortable against the wall than she is in the middle of the floor. Wasn't it you who said last summer that the wallflower now is the girl who has to dance all the time, who, in the delightful and poetic phrase, is "stuck" and can't get rid of her partner, nor he of her? If it weren't so tragic it would be comic to see the curious coldness and stillness in the eyes of boys in a stag line, except when certain girls pass in front of them.

I don't know an intelligent parent who wouldn't like to do something about it. But the obvious thing isn't always the wise one. We had one taste of that last summer when Mrs. White put her foot down and insisted that that niece of hers, Christel, be included in the Fairchilds' houseparty, because the families were old friends. You warned me how it would work out and I knew you were right when I saw the girl's face at the dance that last night. In my nightmares she's dancing yet with the same boy. Of course if a girl has the humor and courage of Marjorie Blair, she doesn't take it so hard. I've always been much amused by that story about Marjorie's bad evening when nobody cut in on her and she stood it as long as she could and then offered a boy a dime if he would. It was a big price for him but I suppose she got her money's worth when the whole male population cut in after that. But, as you said at the time, that trick can only be played once. It's an individual victory and not a breaking down of the system.

After I read your letter, I wondered how it would work if you gave a dance for Ruth and furnished every boy and girl with an old-style program and pencil and had short dances with one encore for each. I considered it seriously but I decided they'd take it as a kind of fancy-dress idea and we couldn't hold them to it throughout the evening. West Point seems to be the only place where they still have program dances. Does that prove, by the way, that it takes an army to protect helpless girls?

I think the first mistake was made when we drew such a sharp line of demarcation between ages and began to think that older people were only a nuisance at parties for young people. No doubt they were tiresome and still would be, but they were also a social protection. Now things have gone so far that it's become very difficult to interfere with the current customs, unless a party is rowdy or obnoxious. I suppose that we older ones were so busy enjoying ourselves that we really didn't pay any attention to the new rules for the younger people until they were coded and accepted and making things difficult for our children.

That's by way of an apology to your generation, but I know it doesn't answer your worried question as to what we are going to do to insure Ruth Beckwith a gay holiday. You say that she's not a very good dancer and that will make it harder. But from the look of her she must have other kinds of ability to make up for that. She must have qualities of friendliness and companionship for all you girls like her, and those are the things, by the way, that men look for in women they marry, sometimes before and always afterward. Isn't it too bad Mark won't be home? He would be such a help. You could count on him to entertain a guest of yours if you asked him to do it.

Suppose we ask a few of your crowd to dinner here before that first big party on the twenty-fourth. Choose a partner for Ruth that you can count on. He ought to be interested in something besides the wave in a girl's hair and the fleetness of her foot, if you know such a boy. And pass the word around that you don't want Ruth neglected. It's part of civilized social life to help entertain strangers and guests, and your friends are quite old enough to know that.

Try it out, but I wouldn't force things too far. You can't scold boys—still less men—into liking girls. You can demand courtesy but that's all. Anything beyond that has to be voluntary. All girls know the difference, and Ruth is too self-respecting to want to be made a duty. If she really has a difficult time at the first dance, I wouldn't insist that she go to many more, or spend my holiday wangling my way into them and wangling my way out. It isn't worth the nervous strain.

I suppose it's idle to tell you or Ruth, both imminently confronted with five or six dances, that a girl who goes to none of them, or who is "stuck" at one of them, may have a greater emotional future and far more interesting future love affairs than the girl whose shoulders are fingerprinted by every boy in the room at a party. But it's true. If you knew what many of the girls who were most popular in my group when I was your age look like now you would have an idea of how such things work out. I'll have to ask you to take this on faith, that real charm and emotional experience can not be measured by a girl's obvious popularity or the lack of it. Never forget that.

All very well, but you can't spend a holiday looking into Ruth's future. I can hear you ask skeptically what else there is to do if you don't go to the dances. We aren't very imaginative about amusements for girls who don't follow—or foxtrot—the beaten track.

If you like, you can fill this vacation with

amusements that you never have time for when you are going to bed at four every night and getting up at eleven. You can do things that would feature that natural vigor of Ruth's. She'd look very well in a ski suit, for example, and you can have a winter house-party at the cabin if you want one.

You don't have to act like old maids. I may be wrong, but I think you would be able, without a great deal of effort, to get many boys to come to that sort of party and like it. One of them told me not long ago that he was sick to death of dances. "Cutting in on the same girls night after night," he said drearily. "Well," I said, "why not cut in on some of the others?" He looked so dismayed that I saw that I had proposed the unmentionable! But that young fellow would be very glad of a variation in his social life. He's tired of losing his sleep. He knows there must be better times than the ones he's having. And he's certainly right.

Come home by the earliest train and bring Ruth and be perfectly fearless about it. That seems a large word for such a small situation and yet I don't think it's out of place. Social life is like that. If you don't control it fearlessly, it's apt to bully you.

Christmas gives us a holiday for happiness, and that's what we should use it for, not for competitions and worries. I shall be at the station to meet you. You will know me by the holly in my buttonhole.

Love,

MOTHER

III

OVERDRAFT

III

DEAR SUSAN: Your very full explana-
tions about the new evening coat, the
overdraft in your bank account and the general state of your finances are all here, kind-
ness of air mail. There is a bill for you from
the dry-cleaners here too. I suppose it has
something to do with the cleaning of your
clothes at Christmas time. I'm forwarding it
to you and I hope it hasn't the bad taste to
arrive on Valentine's Day.

That was a very plausible letter. Good bar-
gains like that do turn up in February and
I know how well gold lamé with a fur collar

[64]

would set off the head and shoulders of a blond young person with a good skin. In fact I got to thinking of that picture with so much interest that I had to remind myself callously that the fact at issue is that you are in debt, overdrawn and have no money rightfully coming to you for about eighteen days.

Of course you have the coat! Technically it belongs to you, though full title still must rest with the shop that hasn't been entirely paid for it, and the bank may have some claim on a few gold threads. You say that they were glad to give you credit at the shop. I wonder. They probably trust the fact that you are in a good, respectable college. Or they believe your parents will stand back of a purchase even if you shouldn't have made it.

As I remember, you and I spent a long time considering what your allowance ought to be. You said it was large enough. You

[65]

knew that it was much less than many of your friends have to spend. But you were sure that it would take care of all your personal expenses if we paid college fees and railway fares. Anyway, it was all we could afford to give you and you were satisfied. But here we are already with a condition of failure on our hands.

Yes, I know that you don't consider it that. By the end of April this elegant garment will be paid for in full, and you now have juggled your original budget until you think that you can get along on less than you estimated for other expenses. Perhaps you can, unless something else turns up that you think must be bought because it is so becoming or such a good bargain.

Those two arguments have led more women to lead dishonest lives than any others in the world. I was thinking of it the other day, before I had your letter, in connection with the Davis Wades.

Did you know that they are going to get a divorce? I'm very sorry about it. They were so much in love. But apparently Kitty was just too expensive for poor Davis. They got to the point where they quarrelled incessantly about money, and one day Davis called up every shop in town and cut off her credit. It was a horrid business but I don't think he knew what else to do. Kitty couldn't resist buying what she wanted or what someone told her she wanted. But it was bitterly humiliating for her, and she left him and went home to her family and started suit for divorce.

I don't want to make moral lessons out of your friends' tragedies, but it seems to me that case makes one thing very clear. Spending power is almost as important as earning power. A person who can spend money well is a very useful citizen. One reason this country is in such a bad state of nerves today is that so many people were like Kitty Wade, spending money according to their desires instead of according to their resources.

When you went back to college, and until you saw this particular evening wrap, you didn't think you needed one. You had the black velvet for warmish weather, and your winter coat seemed to be all right for both day and night wear. It was also on the theory that you didn't need any more expensive things until spring that you bought that brown plaid wool dress. You wanted it and it looked well on you and you were prepared to do without other things in order to have it. Now you feel the same way about this coat. That can't go on indefinitely.

I know why you want it. It would be fun to have a golden wrap when you go to that prom with Mark next month, and it would make you feel very grand and important passing doormen. Mark's eyes would probably stick out at the sight of you. But it isn't very fair to him, if he should happen to be the man you marry. You aren't making a very good preparation for happiness with a man if you go into debt and are overdrawn at the bank in order to delight his eyes. You don't delight them long by those methods.

Susan dear, if you can't keep your desires within your allowance now, the chances are that you couldn't keep them within the limits of a fortune. It isn't a question of how much money you have, but how you handle it. I've known plenty of rich women who were always in money difficulties. This isn't a question of forty-five dollars—thirty-nine dollars and fifty cents, I mean. It's a question of whether you can control your desires or whether you are going to spend a good part of your life making excuses for the trouble you get into because of them.

The world is full of beautiful and becoming things and they'll be constantly pressed on your attention. But don't begin to cheat. The minute you take an article from a shop that you can not pay for, it's just a form of shop-lifting, no matter if you still have credit. And if you draw checks on a bank for more money than you have in it, it's an ugly business.

The point at which I almost break down is that I would so like to see you in that coat. I would like to do a little personal cheating, and help you buy it. But I am not going to indulge myself. I shall cover the overdraft and I shall have to take that much from your allowance next month. It makes a big hole in it, doesn't it? What are you going to do about new shoes and this impatient cleaning bill?

You know—or at least I do—that the evening coat may not be as gratifying as you think. I doubt if Mark needs to be dazzled into greater affection for you. And doormen simply don't remember. If there is time and you've not had it altered, why don't you send it back to the shop with a frank note? If you can't do that, regard it as your big dissipation in clothes and try to get enough pleasure out of being dashing to make up for wearing your old evening dress in the Easter vacation.

I know just how it is. Once I bought one of those coats myself. Mine was trimmed with silver fox.

Love,

MOTHER

IV

EARLY MARRIAGE

IV

DEAREST SUSAN: It wasn't such surprising news. For quite a long while you've been singling Mark out as the most important man you knew. There were so many signs, your interest in his studying law, your indignation when you thought he made himself ridiculous over that Cleveland girl, which showed that you were beginning to consider him almost unconsciously as a man you might marry. Now after this Easter holiday, with its sunshine and lilies and eagerness to begin another season, you both have decided that you want to get married right away and you ask me not to say that you are too young.

I won't say that. I don't think you are too young. You're nineteen (twenty in June) and Mark is three years older. Certainly that's not too young for marriage biologically, though we have tampered with biology more or less by our system of educating girls as well as men, and also by this long-continued depression in business which makes it so hard for marriages to earn their way as they should. And of course I want you to marry. I think that marriage is the best material out of which any woman can make a beautiful and becoming life.

But this isn't a blessing on any such immediacy as you propose. For though I don't think you are too young, I don't think you are ready to be married. You are in college. Mark is still studying, and though you tell me he

can get a job now and go back to his studying later, there's a disorderly impatience
about these plans that I don't like. I think
you should wait for at least a year.

It is true that the happiest marriages are
sometimes very young ones. This happened
even more frequently before we began to ad-
vertise and insist that marriage was so full of
dreadful and obscure problems that it was
almost beyond human control. A great many
simple women used to manage it very well,
problems and all. You remember Mrs. Quen-
tin? She married at eighteen and she's had
far more than her share of burdens, and a
gayish husband, but she is the youngest-look-
ing and most serene woman for her age that
I know. That's because she's loved one man
for so long, and began so early. It's a great
aid to beauty.

There is something suitable about young

marriages, too. Shopping around for a husband has made many a spinster. That was true of your aunt Elinor. She could have married at least three men. But it was her passion for perfection that made the trouble, and that got worse as she became older and less flexible. She really wanted to marry, but the man had to meet her exact standard of weights and measures. She waited for the Right Man to come along, and waiting for him is one of those superstitions which is always noticed when it does work but never noticed when it fails.

But though I tell you these things in favor of early marriages, don't think I believe in hasty or greedy ones. You have only to look at Marjorie Allen to see how those turn out. This is her third marriage before thirty and I don't believe that anyone thinks that this will last better than the first two. Her mother was mourning about that to me yesterday, saying that she wished she had kept Marjorie longer in school, or sent her to college. With your letter in my mind I all but told her that wasn't the answer! The trouble with Marjorie was apparent at the start. I remember that she said at her own bridal dinner, "Well, if it doesn't work out, divorces come easy!"

She had no conviction of permanence, and without that marriage is never more than a cheap adventure in sex. That's why there are two kinds of early marriages, the ones that truly are romances and the ones which simply legalize episodes of passion. I am not sure which this would be for you and Mark. I don't think even you know.

Are you sure that you are ready to promise each other all the fidelity and tolerance and endurance that marriage needs if it is not to become a horror? Don't think you can get along without those things, or with a smattering of them. Marriage will not spare your body or your mind or your spirit. It will take concentration, and neither you nor Mark so far has been a very concentrated person. Before Mark became fond of you he had a good many enthusiasms over other girls. And as for you, it may seem unfair to remind you of this but I think I'll do it anyway. Do you remember how you felt a year ago about a young man called Henry? There was a week when everyone in the house was in the way. A very nice dancer, that Henry! I always remember how he could twirl without losing his effect of manliness. I'm not joking. I'm just trying to make you remember that intensity of feeling comes and then goes, especially when your feelings are young and new. There ought to be more than such personal eagerness when you contemplate marriage.

Also you propose to let Mark give up his study of law and take a job that he doesn't like so that he can provide for you. In order to build up a life together, you begin by tearing down the very foundations of his planned career. You write that he will go back to the law in a year or two. Don't prophesy, darling. Human relations do strange things to people.

What do you lose by waiting? Are you afraid that you may love him less? Then don't trust your future to such an unsure feeling. Or do you think that you might lose Mark to some other girl? Well, if you can only keep him by satisfying his passion you can not keep him very long, whether you marry him or not.

It may seem queer to you but I hate to have you miss the waiting. Provided that you do not harass or over-stimulate each other, looking forward to marriage is one of the pleasantest times you'll ever know. There is a habit of gulping courtship that is not good for the emotions. When I ask you to wait I do not ask you to suffer. Nor do I ask any more of Mark than a man should give a girl he means to marry, proof of his powers of patience and steadiness in devotion.

I can not do more than ask. You are of age and you must make the decision. But I would not allow you to remain in college after you marry, as you vaguely suggest. It would not be fair to your work, your health, to Mark or to marriage. You must not make marriage into a week-end. It was meant for a life. Tell Mark what I think. I like him even more for wanting to marry my daughter.

Love to you both,

MOTHER

V

PASSION OR LOVE

V

April 12, 1935

DEAR SUSAN: There is no reason for you to be so distressed. You are working yourself up into a state of excessive worry over—no, I must not write that it is nothing. What happened to you was important but it was not unusual or disastrous. Because you are engaged to Mark though you have so wisely decided not to marry for several years, you feel that there was something disloyal and cheap in being attracted so greatly by this other young man whose name you do not mention. It has made you distrust your emotions and rather discredit them. And that is a pity.

If I could explain this backwards to you, so that you, like myself, could look over the shoulder of experience, you'd see so quickly what really did happen. There was a flare of passionate feeling between you and that stranger. There's nothing in that which isn't as old and as inevitable as the nature of men and women. You kept the situation under control and it did no great harm, except in so far as it's troubling you now and keeping you from giving full attention to the things you should be doing.

I was wishing only the other day that there were some way to explain to you the difference between passion and love. Now you've shown yourself the difference. You didn't love this young passer-by and you know it. He is not, you write, the kind of man you'd ever want to marry.

It is rather good luck for both men and women that they don't have to marry all the people to whom at one time and another they are attracted sentimentally or passionately. If it were necessary, monogamy would certainly have to go. But fortunately we don't marry like that. And, though this may seem a rash thing for a mother to say to a daughter, a number of these passing attractions and emotions are not harmful, unless they are allowed the full rights of love. In fact they may even do good. They show you the difference between what you want permanently and what will last through a week-end.

Don't imagine that I'd write so reassuringly if I thought you'd lost either control or judgment. You know very well what I think of chastity and personal purity. Purity is a composite virtue of the body and mind and it long survives the people who mock at it. It is a sturdy, durable virtue, and more broad-minded than is often understood. Cleo Vare, for example, in spite of what you may have heard about her unconventionalities, is a very pure-minded woman. There is a directness and honesty in her relations with both men and women, a lack of anything shifty or promiscuous which puts her, to my thinking, far above women who are often more discreet.

Let me see if I can explain this very simply. Most normal women and girls are exposed to unexpected flurries of passion. There is no escape from it, unless you shut your life off from normal contacts and that has a bad, corrosive effect. Passion is a part of life and its intensity varies with the temperament of every individual. It keeps living from being dull or over-monotonous or too sure of itself. It is responsible for many exciting adventures, much poetry and great drama.

But on the other hand passion has a great deal of cruelty and suffering and many illegitimate children to account for. For there are two things not to be forgotten. Passion is transient and it is irresponsible. That is how you tell the difference between it and love, and sometimes you can't tell at first glance. For passion also is a great actor. It strikes attitudes. It often pretends it is the most permanent of feelings, unless it is the worldly sort that makes a fetish of the transitory and believes in a new emotion every day. But ordinarily passion thinks that it can do anything, and the more unsafe and higher its perch the louder it crows. I rather like it for its cockiness and exaltation. But as for trusting it, I wouldn't for a minute, unless it was backed by love.

There is something about love which is altogether different in texture. You can feel the silk threads of tenderness in love, as well as the eagerness, the desire to preserve as well as to enjoy, and to do the best thing for the loved person even with sacrifice. I have been far more convinced that there is truly deep feeling between you and Mark since the two of you decided that it would not be best for the future of either of you to marry now. In your letters of explanation to me, both you and Mark were arguing for the other's good.

Of course I don't mean that passion doesn't go along with love or stay with marriage. It must. But it can not substitute for love. I have so often seen passion thinking it was as strong as love. It isn't. It can not carry the load of caring for another person through all the dullness and monotonies that are part of every day. It is charming and irresistible in the room when the lights are right and the fire burning well. But passion with its collar off, having to fix the furnace, exposed to a cold in its head, shows up badly.

Thinking of common colds reminds me that the man who probably cared most for me once wrote me in a letter, "I was thinking yesterday of what I could do for you if you were a little ill, if you should have a cold." In my day I have had a good many letters from men, and their charming, often repetitive (sometimes plagiarized) statements have blurred. But that more than twenty-year-old sentence still stands out in my mind. I knew he was really in love with me when he wrote that, and that even when I wasn't pretty or intelligent or good-humored, he still would care!

That is what I want for you and what you instinctively want. But this young man has upset you a little. You turned back to your feeling for Mark with more respect. But now you want Mark to bring you the excitement which the other young man supplied and, along with it, much more. You want Mark to feel about you as dramatically as this Black Knight did.

You didn't write that. It was between the lines. You are a little afraid that Mark might be dull. So he may be. And so may you be! You should not marry him at all unless he can stir your senses deeply, and you his. You should not marry him unless beyond that stir of the senses you are sure that he will try to give you such permanence of devotion as you must try to offer him, a permanence so great and true that a look of admiration or a few hours of pleasure or stimulation in the company of other men and women will only give you more to offer each other.

Perhaps next time such an incident as this may happen between Mark and some other girl. You must think of that too.

Love,

MOTHER

VI

A JOB OF HER OWN

VI

June 2, 1935

DEAR SUSAN: I don't wonder that you were excited. Such things don't happen very often to girls in college, especially during these hard times. You must have been doing especially good work in chemistry if the head of the department is so strongly advising you to major in it and has practically promised to secure you a laboratory job when you graduate. Isn't it a pleasure to see your education become something more than lessons and examinations and turn into a tool that can be used to earn a living or perhaps carve out a very useful career?

Of course I don't advise you to hesitate. Arrange your courses so as to work toward that end. What you write about wondering if it might be hard to choose between marriage and a career seems to me to be slightly over-dramatized. The notion that a woman's ability to earn her living precludes her having a normal or satisfactory marriage has been disproved many times. More and more, I think, the girl who has no earning ability is going to be at a disadvantage even in marriage.

That is partly because economic conditions are so uncertain that all those who have a chance to earn or a special capability should be able and ready to exercise it in an emergency. We assume, and it's quite proper that we should, that Mark will be able to support a wife, and he ought not to marry, for his own self-respect, until he feels that he can. But if he had very bad luck—or unexpected ill-health—how lucky you would be to have an earning capacity then.

I don't mean that I think very highly of some of these arrangements we see around us when two people marry and both keep on with their jobs at the obvious sacrifice of a home. Unless it is necessary for money reasons, or unless her work is too valuable to society to be interrupted, or too individual to be turned over to someone else (and that's pretty rare) a girl who marries ought to make her marriage her main job. She ought to give it most of her time and the best of her energy, and she can't do it if she's employed and being paid to give just those same things to her employer.

There's much more to marriage than running the vacuum cleaner over the rugs. There is the creation of an environment which has never existed before because those two people have never been married before, and every marriage is different from every other one. Usually and naturally there are children. That takes health and devotion. And a man wants more from a woman than he ever knows how to ask for. He wants someone to restore his courage every other day, and build up his faith in himself. It's almost impossible for a girl who herself is at a desk eight hours a day to do that. It's not just because she's tired but because she too needs the same things that the man is asking her to give him. In marriage, and especially at the beginning of marriage, either the husband or wife must be willing to make the outside-the-home interests of the other predominant. Biology hasn't changed enough to make it a good thing for the man to put his wife's work first, as a usual thing.

Do I seem to be contradicting myself? I'm not. I'll illustrate. Someone was telling me yesterday of how desperately Ellen Gentin is trying to find something to do. Jim hasn't anything left and no one can say that is his fault. Ellen is bright and intelligent but she doesn't know how to do anything. She has no value in the world of jobs and yet she probably had thousands of dollars spent on her school fees alone. But today, though she has health and willingness, she doesn't know where to turn for a living in a world that asks for training and recommendations.

That's one case. On the other hand there is that young, cool (or is it cold?) Martha Barrett who married Peter Eccleston. Peter is a gentle, kindly man and it seems a pity to hear about his hanging around his club every afternoon until Martha gets through with her very unimportant work. It's nonsense for that pair

to live in an apartment hotel and eat in a public restaurant most of the time. Martha won't
give up her bookshop, though Peter could
quite well take care of her, and dozens of
girls would be glad to step into her place in
the shop. What Martha ought to be doing is
building up Peter. She ought to make him
less vague and more responsible—or he'll get
worse—and she could do it if she'd turn the
energy that goes into her bookshop on Peter.
And bearing a child would do more for Martha than any number of sales slips.

You see what's wrong in both those cases.
It's fine that Martha can run a shop. But this
isn't the time for her to do it. On the other
hand, if Ellen had only been definitely trained
to develop herself so that she could sell books,
she wouldn't be in a panic today.

What you ought to do is to go ahead and
prepare yourself and your capabilities for

practical and useful work. That doesn't do Mark any harm and it's insurance for both of you. But when you marry him, put his interests first. Let the science of chemistry wait for a while. It will be patient. Later on, especially if you marry young, there may come a period when you can go back to it.

You may go back to it because you will find that you have increasing leisure as you get fully adjusted to marriage and my grandchildren grow older. The thing to do in the meantime is not to get mentally indolent as so many women do. They let their minds rust and there's no necessity for that.

In any case, don't quarrel with your future. It's very illbred. Just keep on with your work and direct it toward its greatest possible usefulness. It will give you a direct relation to life and progress. Every woman should have that, as well as the feeling that she won't be

[97]

helpless if a man's income is not available for her to spend.

But don't ever make your work into Mark's rival.

Love, and be brilliant,

MOTHER

VII

PETTING

VII

DEAR SUSAN: We left too many things unfinished, particularly conversations. The doorbell and the telephone kept breaking them up during that last week you were home. But the half hour we had together while you were packing and discussing "petting" stays in my mind. I keep thinking of the firm way you put that blue evening dress on a trunk hanger and said, "I don't see the harm in it." You weren't speaking of the dress. But it evidently reminded you of an occasion, or a person, or a previous argument.

At first I thought I would lay the subject

[100]

aside until I saw you again. But it's better not. You wear the dress often and perhaps a dangerous philosophy is one of the accessories that goes with it. Also you asked two questions that I didn't get a chance to answer. One was: "What is the harm in it?" Then you went on to say, after a comment I made: "Well, what is going too far? Times have changed, mother."

I know what you mean by that final caution. We have passed the days when a kiss was almost the equivalent of an engagement ring, or when a girl boxed a man's ears for putting his arm around her. All this petting or necking—choose your own word—is much more common and casual than was formerly true among civilized people. Petting and necking are cheap and ineffective words. I always hate to say them or to write them. And yet they are probably adequate and rather exact for what they describe. It certainly isn't love-making. Petting has become a regularized pastime among young people, and even less charmingly, among those who aren't young.

I hope you won't write off my point of view as "dated." Physiology is what it always has been, and psychology has been only slightly altered. If there was harm in lack of physical reserve twenty years ago, there still is harm. One bad result is the dulling and blunting of sensation that comes from any kind of promiscuity or from over-indulgence of the senses. Another is the untimely and futile and often cruel sharpening of physical appetites. Does it seem contradictory to say that petting dulls sensation and yet increases appetite? That is what happens. A girl who starts it or is used to it rarely wants to stop, and sometimes she can't because the habit has a physical hold on her. Yet she gets less pleasure or value out of a caress than a girl who has maintained reserves. There is further harm in the fact that she piles up memories of intimacies that may be embarrassing and perhaps shameful in a few years or even a few months, when the attraction that led to them no longer exists. And finally, a girl's reputation among boys and men is still valuable to her. You know that. I've heard you say so. No man or boy will protect a girl who makes no effort to protect herself. She will be at the mercy of his gossip and his casual desires. If a man knows that he can not have a girl for himself, his attitude toward her is the one that men have always had toward women of easy virtue, perhaps not quite as contemptuous as it used to be, but still selfish and hard. He will take as much as he can get from her and give as little as possible in return. This may not be fair but it is the way things are.

One defense of petting is that it is necessary if a girl does not want to be considered a stick or a prude and, as a result, left out of good times. Well, she doesn't have to be a prude and yet she can have restraint. Once last summer I came downstairs when you had some people in the house and saw Joan and Sam dancing in the hall. As they finished the dance he gave her a kiss and she took it and they both laughed and looked so happy and gay that I stood there admiring them. There was nothing feverish or over-excited or furtive about it. Joan is always popular and she's friendly and affectionate and no doubt often tender with the boys she knows. But I never worry about her. I do worry about Clarice. When that girl goes out in the garden with a boy I want to go after her and bring her back. And she always is disappearing toward dark gardens and parked cars. I shall always think of her as disappearing.

But I suppose that when you asked that straight question as to what "going too far" was or should be, you were not thinking of Clarice, that gently reared girl whom I heard described by some boys as a "public neck!" You were wondering whether a girl who is deeply fond of one man should establish limits in her conduct with him, and what they should be. Perhaps you were thinking of how far you and Mark should go. I can suggest a test. When you wonder whether or not you are going too far, you may be sure that you are. It is fear or shame that makes you wonder.

This isn't merely a matter of what is called "safety." It is a premature breaking down of reserves that can never be built up again once they are destroyed. Instinctively you know that. Nature only gives a girl or a woman a certain amount of delicacy and a certain amount of control. If she throws those things away she has to get along without them from then on, and this habit of petting (again not love) makes her throw them away too soon or too carelessly. Love doesn't ask for the best it can ever have in too much of a hurry.

You may say that this is not practical advice as to what to do in a given situation, or that it doesn't tell you how to keep from going too far. I haven't given you a rule since I told you categorically as a little girl that you must make boys keep their hands off you. You've no doubt outgrown that instruction and I've been relying, perhaps too long, on your good taste and control. But I can give you a few more rules, if you would like to have them.

One would be this: Don't let a boy who has been drinking caress you. It doesn't mean anything and there is no reason why you should be part of his drink.

Don't let a boy who has a reputation for making conquests add you to his list. This wouldn't apply to you now, perhaps, but it is worth keeping in mind.

Don't think you can make a conquest by letting a boy be free with your body.

Don't start petting because you are sorry for a boy or man. That's a very poor reason. It doesn't help him very much in the end, even though you both might think it would in the beginning.

Don't get affectionate because it's late at night.

Don't give away your future to make an hour more stimulating.

These are simple directions, but if you follow them you can still find plenty of room for gayety and affection and the preliminaries of love. Beyond these warnings, I must add that what is quite unwise for a person of one temperament and age is not for another, and

you must know yourself. Very young girls
certainly should be controlled by definite pro-
hibitions. I have never been sorry that I told
you in so many words, when you were an obe-
dient little girl, to keep boys from handling
you. A girl who does that until she is fifteen
or sixteen isn't apt to go too far when she is
twenty. The trouble is that girls begin this
petting when they are only children and it is
not a child's game.

It's those girls I am sorry for. You can't say
there's no harm in petting when you see what
happens to them. They are the sad heroines of
constant scandals and breakdowns. They are
the wretched, restless, unscrupulous girls
turned loose in the world to make trouble.
You see there's bound to be harm in any practice which makes the relationships between
men and women less fine and less individual.
Give that a personal test every now and then.

Ask yourself whether you could say, if you found Mark and another girl violently engaged in petting, "There's no harm in it."

I don't believe you could. You know you couldn't!

Love,

MOTHER

VIII

DRINKING

VIII

DEAR SUSAN: Thank you for writing
such a frank answer to my letter. I'm
glad that you agree on most points, even if
you do argue the one about drinking. You say
that if a girl never let a man who had been
drinking touch her that she might have to go
to her grave untouched; and that a girl can
always handle a man who's been drinking if
she herself keeps her head. The story of what
happened to you over that week-end is certainly an illustration of that, and in a way I
was proud of you. And yet, though I can't
help admiring your tolerance and your cool

[111]

young sufficiency, it gives me a horrid feeling to think of my daughter in a strange tavern with a young man who was drinking until he couldn't drive his car or even keep awake. Maybe he is as brilliant as you and Mark say, and as forgivable, but I somehow don't feel his charm at this distance.

Every little while I am brought up short by the realization that when a young man takes a girl out for a social evening they are apt to spend part of it in a saloon. I know they aren't called saloons since repeal. They're called Flame Bars or Golden Pitchers or Egyptian Rooms or Tony's Place. But all the Tonies in the world can't change the fundamental purposes of their establishments. Nor do they want to. They are public drinking places, and in the midst of the red leather couches and checked tablecloths alcohol is up to its usual tricks, making some people gay, some amorous, some quarrelsome and putting others to sleep.

I will say this before I go on. I am continually amazed at the control and good temper and skill of most of you girls. Of course there are exceptions. The other night I saw a girl we both know at the Majestic Hotel. I won't tell you who it was. I don't believe in spreading scandal, even to you. But she is normally pretty and that night she looked indescribably unattractive. Her face was pallid and her eyes narrowed and she had a dissolute lack of charm. The only people, men or girls, who could possibly have considered her attractive were those as far gone as she was. I kept thinking that if she only had an idea of how she looked she would never again have anything to drink stronger than sarsaparilla. But of course she didn't know. How could she? All the mirrors in the world couldn't have told her. Her eyes were out of focus and her imagination distorting everything.

Drinking is definitely part of the social life of the United States just now. People can deplore and decry that until they are hoarse without changing the fact. If it is changed it will be because of a shift of mood on the part of young people like yourself.

I saw some figures the other day to the effect that temperance was on the increase and they seemed to have a lot of proof back of them. I hope it means that young people are getting more temperate. For much as I dislike to see any human beings wasted through drinking, if I had to make a choice I'd scrap the older ones. They ought to know better.

The first thing to find out about alcohol is not which vintages of wine are best, or the way to make a cocktail, but what it does to you in physical and psychological and perhaps moral ways. And then, in the old phrase, govern yourself accordingly. Govern is the word.

Perhaps you ought not to drink at all. One cocktail or one highball may make a changeling out of you, eager for another drink, careless of what is said or done, taking risks that are dangerous. But it may be that if you are old enough and healthy and have a stable nervous system, you can take a drink or two without being harmed or even much affected. Often that seems the natural and sociable thing to do, as it must have seemed to you the other night. You say that you were "perfectly all right." I don't doubt it. I refuse to doubt it, though I have so often heard people claim that they were "perfectly all right" when they weren't that my faith in the words is permanently shaken.

I've tried to be practical about this matter

of drinking and, knowing that you couldn't have a separate world even if I wanted it, to fit you for the one you would live in and for the habits of people you would meet. Do you remember when you had your first glass of sherry one Christmas? Then the year when you first went to college you promised me that you would drink no cocktails, no matter who served them or where you might be visiting. But as you grew older that seemed over-rigid, so we decided that on special occasions I would let you have one drink. Now we've reached the point where I must believe that you have sufficient knowledge both of yourself and the power of alcohol so that you can decide on what occasions you will take a drink and whether it will be one or two. In my heart I would rather that you never took one. With my mind I know that won't be the case. But there's just one rule about drinking that you'll never grow too old to obey. Never take a drink when you feel you can't get along without one. You must be the boss.

The other thing to know about alcohol in addition to what it does to you is that you can not count on what it may do to other people. You found out the other night what it did to one young man, Mark's highly recommended friend whose ears I yearn to box. Always remember that when people are drinking, situations are never normal. They may be gay and amusing but you can not tell what is happening in the minds and bodies of other people and you must be on your guard. You can never trust a person who is drinking to be a completely competent escort. I remember you said last summer that you didn't like Philip Jeffrey much but that he always got a girl home from a party. It was certainly a negative recommendation, but again it shows what situations you meet even in commonplace, middle-class groups like ours.

I think you girls are inclined to be much too tolerant of the ways boys and men drink when they are your escorts. What do you get out of it? It is very tiresome to be with a man who is high—or possibly low. It can't mean coherent conversations, and the attention you get is fuddled and the dancing bad. Yet girls like yourself, who drink little or nothing, spend long hours with young men who grow less interesting with every glass they put to their lips and, what is more, will probably add the thought of you to their general grudge against the world next day. You can't expect any gratitude from a drunken man. If the one of whom you were so considerate the other night thinks of you at all now, the chances are that he may be blaming you for the whole incident.

I'll give you one bit of advice. Men often

drink because they think it's expected of them. If you have a soft drink or a glass of tomato juice, some of them would be glad to join you. Men have a secret weakness for taking care of themselves. I know. I'm always surprised to see how many men will take tea if tea happens to be competing with cocktails. Not always, of course, but often.

There has always been a battle between alcohol and women. Women have tried to manage it by every device, from hatchets to the present tolerance. Liquor isn't kind to women. It ravages their looks and their loves and their homes. The truce you girls make with it now, the attempt to make it a gay companion, may be all right if you never trust it or let it get the better of you. But don't think it will ever be your friend. Because it won't be.

Love,

MOTHER

IX

PAY YOUR OWN WAY

IX

DEAR SUSAN: So Mark let you pay for your own dinner and you had told him that was what you wanted to do but none the less it got on your nerves. Is the trouble with you or with him, you want to know. Is it false pride in you, or is Mark lacking in self-respect?

You've stumbled over a condition of affairs which is making a great deal of trouble between girls and young men, before they are married and after they're married. It's partly due to the fact that times are hard, and partly because women earn money and handle it for themselves. This is just a matter of a dinner-

[121]

check now and doesn't matter greatly. But sooner or later, especially if you intend to earn money that first year after you are out of school and Mark hasn't much to spend for a while, the problem will be much more serious.

It is reason working against instinct. You knew that Mark couldn't afford to take you out for dinner. You could go only if you paid for your meal and he for his. Yet, when that was reasonably agreed upon, your instinct began to hate the situation in which the man who was your escort was paying nothing for the pleasure of your company but got it free, and all sorts of doubts began to rouse themselves.

You aren't the only girl who feels that way. Do you remember a girl called Evelyn Sands in your uncle Fred's office, who looked like a lily and was probably the most efficient secretary he ever had? He was very much down in the mouth when he heard that she was going to be married, and then very much up in the mouth because she told him one day that she had changed her mind. But I didn't like the last news so well. I knew that Evelyn had really been in love, and she is one of my favorite girls—her mother used to be a friend of mine in grade school and was an even lovelier lily. Somehow, to think of Evelyn going on in your uncle Fred's office indefinitely, remembering all the things he forgets, didn't seem future enough for her. So I made an excuse to call on him when I knew he was out of town, and talked to her. I asked her why she had changed her mind and mentioned the fact that the young man had certainly seemed very much in love with her. I'd seen the two of them together.

She went a little paler and didn't say any-

thing. Then she said everything, and some of
it I can tell to you and some I can't. But the
reason for the break was that he had let her
do everything for herself and then had borrowed a little money from her and not paid it
back. She said: "He doesn't mind any more
when I pay my way. He did at first and then
he cared less and less. It isn't the money I
grudge, but how can I respect a man who lets
me pay not only for my own meals but for
his? What would happen after we were married? I'd rather let him go now than hate him
afterwards."

She wasn't perfectly sure of that last state-
ment, poor thing. She was having a dreadful
time. She explained him to me, defended him.
"Of course he hasn't much money," she told
me. "I know that. And he was out of a job
when he borrowed that money. I wanted to
help him. But he takes so much for granted!"

Men do that. Just last night I happened to be at the same dinner-party with the Dick Blaines. You know their financial arrangements as everyone does. He lives on her fortune and they seem to be happy. But there is a softening of fibre in Dick Blaines that I don't like. He hated his wife's money at first, and now he just takes it for granted, like Evelyn's young man.

You too had a taste of it the other night. Now suppose for example that Mark can't make a living and you can. How will it work out in your own case? Are you willing to support him? Of course every instinct in you will rise to say that you certainly would never support an able-bodied man. I'd hate to see you do it. Yet thousands of girls and women are doing it, and something in them is shrivelling all the time.

It isn't the fault of most men and boys,

though there are loafers who take advantage of women. But as I tried to explain to Evelyn, it's harder for men to care for women than it used to be. The old-fashioned courting was arranged like this: The man came to see the girl in her house (at no expense to him) night after night. They didn't go to restaurants. They didn't go to movies. The girl made preparations for her own contribution to the marriage expenses, hemmed linen, made clothes. Her parents were prepared to give her a dowry or a settlement. The young man was assuming the burden of supporting a woman, but the girl's father knew it was a burden and, since it was being lifted from his shoulders, he made such compensations as he could. Everyone thought this was proper. If a man married a girl who had no dowry, he was known to be irresistibly in love, but either rich himself or possibly not very wise.

Customs changed and women began to earn money, as you plan to do, and as the efficient lily of an Evelyn already does. She has, in fact, been earning a little more than the man to whom she was engaged. Do you see what happens to the natural psychology? The man can't court her in her father's parlor. She hasn't a father or a parlor. (You have a parlor but you never sit in it!) No, both you and Evelyn have to be taken out for entertainment by the young men who want to marry you. You aren't fools and you know they haven't much money. So you say you'll pay your own way. Then when you do, and they accept it, you begin to burn up with the feeling of not having what that courted girl of long ago was given.

You can't have it both ways. That's all there is to it.

I certainly do not think that you should let

Mark get the habit of having you pay your own way all the time, as if you were another young man. It takes something out of the relationship for him as well as for you. But why not do things that don't cost money, or very little? Go for an occasional walk. Buy some hamburgers and eat them in the park. Go to a band concert. They're free, because of taxes. Let Mark provide for you as well as he can, both now and later.

If you want more, then probably you must pay your own way. Mark can not. If you agree to do that, see your generosity all the way through. Don't go back on it. It is a modern privilege to earn and pay for yourself, handle your own funds. The protected girl with the dowry had to obey her husband in ways that would be intolerable to you. Remember that in normal circumstances a woman can keep an average man from accepting too much or

[128]

leaning on her. As for extraordinary circumstances, nothing will see women and men through those except generosity and affection which is very tender of self-respect. I think that is what Evelyn begins to understand. Her young man's pride was hurt, as well as her own. He pretended to callousness, and after a little it was no longer pretense. She will have to restore something in him, and she can if she loves him enough.

By the way, who wanted most to go to that restaurant the other night—Mark or you?

Love,

MOTHER

X

THE USES OF DELICACY

X

December 10, 1935

DEAR SUSAN: I had plenty to think about on the way home. It was great good luck for me to have been able to make that unexpected trip East, especially since you aren't coming home for Christmas. It would have been altogether too long between glimpses of you. Hard work does seem to agree with you. You look very well and very pretty. My only criticism is that you're not as pleasing to the ear as the eye. Do you realize that some of your talk is pretty loose and decidedly coarse?

It wasn't just your talk. It was that conversation that went on between you and the others that startled me. Naturally I realize that it wasn't for my ears and that it was very embarrassing for everyone when you discovered that night that I was coming down the stairs and must have heard the story Bill Blake was telling all of you.

Curiously enough, I heard the same story last night all over again. It seems to be pursuing me. The train had stopped in some station and the drawingroom door was open next to the section where I was in bed. Regardless of the hush, one man told it to another, and how they all laughed before they took the next drink of many! Bill's story is sweeping the country, and a foul little joke it is.

How many stories like that do you hear and carry around in your mind? Between hearing that story and a few comments that you made about the people at the dance and seeing the book you were travelling with, I've been asking myself if you think you can get along without any mental delicacy.

That is, without a doubt, as unpleasant a book as I've ever read. It is a horrid, provocative, written-for-one-purpose kind of book. I've heard about it and seen advertisements, but it hadn't crossed my path. But finding that you were carrying it affectionately under your arm, I sat down the other night and read it from cover to cover. It has the wrong title. It ought to be called "The Adventures of Peeping Tom." That's all it is. Why you should be interested in the sex reactions of a couple of neurotic, middle-aged people who weren't either beautiful or intelligent, is more than I can see.

Yes, I am scolding. I don't feel like mincing my words. Authors like that don't mince theirs and I'm as good as they are. In fact,

[133]

I'm much better. If you like frankness, I'll give you some myself. How you can read that book and not feel indecent, I do not understand. There is no reason why you should not know all the physical facts that there are to know. But there is a good deal of reason why you should not go over to a house in the neighborhood and climb up on the fire-escape and look in the bedroom windows.

What possible useful contribution could a book like that make to your life? Why should a young girl waste her time on a story written in cheap slang for the most part, and without a page of fine thought in it? I don't like namby-pamby books. But this thing wasn't even good satire. It wasn't robust like Rabelais. It was just unclean.

Now don't tell me that it's a "part of life." It may be, but it need not be a part of your life. You would avoid such people if you saw them, and you'd leave the house in a fury if I asked them to dinner. Murder and rape and all sorts of unmentionable actions—no, apparently they are all mentionable—are part of life, but so are filth and germs and other things you avoid. And do you really read about such people as were in this book in order to round out a knowledge of different kinds of people, or in order to give yourself a vague sex thrill? I think it's the last reason.

I get so annoyed with people who boast about being broadminded. A person of genuine mental breadth never mentions it. Such people are generous and really sophisticated and tolerant and yet selective. They never claim to be broadminded. They are, and it shows in the way they act. But breadth of mind, according to these others, is to have a collection of sex anecdotes, to be unable to blush, to have no skill or delicacy in relating the conversation to the company, and to have a desire to debauch the young. They have no depth of comprehension that enables them to interpret their own miserable stories with pity or understanding of genuine sex psychology. They have no real humor. They can only laugh at anything which cheapens or tricks the most secret and intimate human relations.

Of course it's one way of attracting attention. A few weeks ago I was at dinner with a varied group of people. One of them was no longer young and never very beautiful and she was not getting much notice. So suddenly she began to tell a story. She told it so loudly that everyone had to listen and no one missed a word. It was one of those old anecdotes that has come almost everyone's way—I'd heard it somewhere and it never had been very funny. It was just about exposure, the final point being completely that. Opposite this woman at the table sat another guest who isn't really strait-laced at all. She has read a good deal and travelled everywhere. She's a generous person. The interesting thing was that as far as she was concerned that story wasn't told. She didn't compress her lips or look angry. She just sat there and removed herself mentally while the thing was going on. She didn't either frown or smile. The story fell back from her complete rejection of it into a queer silence, and I think it's the last time that lady will tell it. At least she'll be careful of her company.

I can't bear to have you become coarse. I always remember the first time I visited you in boarding school and there was a sign up on your door: "No Dirty Jokes Told in Here." You have no idea how proud I was of that sign; and to hear you speak of those strangers the other night as if it was rather amusing to find people promiscuous and unchaste, to hear you laugh at that story, to find that book in your possession, gave me a series of shocks.

Of course when I spoke of it to you the other day you said, "I'm not that way, mother. I don't tell stories like that."

But you listen, and that in itself destroys delicacy. You mustn't think delicacy isn't important. If you knew as much about life as I do, you'd know that the coarsest women weep for the loss of delicacy. And no man ever thought more or better of a woman for enjoying a bad story. He just tells her another and classifies her.

That's not the worst of it. You tear down the dignity of your own sex when you tolerate such stories and read such books. It's working against your sex. It's really disloyal. The protection of decency is for everyone,

[138]

for you, for me, for all the girls you know.
Don't let anyone or anything break it down.
And don't do it yourself.

Love,

MOTHER

XI

OTHER PEOPLE'S HOUSES

XI

January 8, 1936

DEAR SUSAN: It is very uncomfortable to be on both sides of a fence, but there I am! What I mean is that I don't think that the criticism of you which so annoyed you is a sound one, but I can see how it might have arisen. Of course you're not trivial, nor is your education an unjustifiable expense to society. But perhaps you gave that impression.

Be fair and consider all the facts. The man who made the caustic comment had to go on what he saw of your behavior. Kate Jeffrey's father is, from all I know of him, a serious business man who has been all over the world, worked hard, and now he is probably troubled beyond your comprehension by the economic situation. During the Christmas holidays he saw his daughter and you, who were her guest, both of you presumably educated and cultivated young women, with apparently no thought in the world except enjoying yourselves. He watched you strewing his car with cigarette ashes, forgetting to turn out electric lights (I'm just guessing, but isn't it accurate?) and wearing astonishing clothes. You gathered around you young men who ate his food and drank his liquor with never a thought of the source of their supplies. Undoubtedly you never came down for breakfast, but you probably woke poor Mr. Jeffrey up a couple of hours before he was ready to get up for his own breakfast by coming back to his house for a few hours' sleep after a party.

The one serious conversation you had at the dinner table with him, ended, you tell me, in stony silence because he has "a closed mind." But I suppose you wiped off the achievement of his entire life as one of the mistakes of a passing social system. Then, when he says that the modern girl, instancing you, is trivial and thin-minded and that giving her an education is a waste of money, you are insulted.

What a ten days the poor man must have had! Kathy hasn't had friends stopping with her before, I suppose, because the Jeffreys have been travelling about such a lot and have never had a permanent home. He isn't as used as I am to waiting indefinitely for the late car to turn in the driveway, nor to the deliberately casual comments on everything, nor to the fact that there are never any cigarettes left about for the aged, nor any cold food (except old pieces of liver) in the ice-box after you get through eating at midnight what you refused at dinner. He's not accustomed to being casual about cigarette holes in his rugs, nor to finding the furniture dragged here and there and left where it doesn't belong. He wouldn't know from all these manifestations that you are the kind of girl who stayed up all night to finish a topic on the stratosphere, or that you really can run a house, as you proved last summer when I was laid up with that little operation. How could he know? No one gave him an inkling. He has to go on circumstantial evidence.

I disagree entirely with his findings. I don't only think but I know that the modern young girl is generous and intelligent and has her eyes open and that we can't possibly spend too much educating her because she responds to information. But you throw dust in our eyes. I was saying something proud about you last summer when the question had arisen among several of us mothers as to whether we were really doing right by our little Nells; and as we were talking outside the Moffat house, a car went by with some of you in it. It was an open car, much too full of your crowd for safety in driving. It wasn't an expensive car but it was very much a pleasure automobile, high-colored, sporting to the full length of its fenders. In the mouth of every girl in the car there was a cigarette.

Agnes Moffat was standing beside me and she gave a kind of snort and said, "There they go! They'll drive through the city, past unemployed men who stand on corners, past women who are wondering if they can hold on to their jobs or their last few dollars. They look spoiled. They look useless. They make people angry. They cause trouble."

That happened just a few days before you went back to college and I didn't bring it up then. It seemed to me that any revision of such conduct could wait until next summer. But I mention it now because it's on the point. When that happened you were going back to college to study hard in a day or two. For all I know, as you drove by you all were talking intelligently about labor problems or the rate of exchange. But you certainly didn't look it. You looked careless and hard and there was something not at all pleasant in all the cigarette waving.

I don't mean to be prudish. I know that you and most of your friends smoke and I've left it to you and your doctor as far as any problem of health goes. There never seemed to me to be any problem of morals involved. But there are a whole lot of people in the world who from previous associations, prejudices if you like, object to seeing women and girls smoke. There is no use in affronting strangers. You wouldn't saunter down the main street with a cigarette in your mouth. It wouldn't be suitable. Then why ride down the middle of a public thoroughfare doing it?

No one looks askance at a woman or girl who smokes in a restaurant. No one objects. But it is not hypocrisy which makes a wise woman keep from lighting a cigarette if she is on the platform at a political meeting, or at the head table of a dinner for an organized charity. This is a matter of courtesy and social adjustment. It is restraint out of consideration for men and women who deplore that particular habit. Surely you can see that it is much better, in the same way, that some bitter, unemployed man shall not carry around with him a picture of a lot of smoking girls in a fast car. It looks like rioting on his misery.

Agnes Moffat is absolutely right. The same thing holds true about this habit of trailing into inexpensive public restaurants in evening clothes, a kind of exhibitionist slumming.

I sometimes think that the impasse between your generation and mine—not, thank heaven, between you and me—is caused largely by such outward signs. You don't show us that you take life seriously or that you know it isn't a party. You have a kind of stoicism which wears almost a carnival mask. It's partly because you're contemptuous of all the useless sobbing that's been done by older people, and it may be partly protective, for fear you yourselves might break down.

But however that may be, the world—and Mr. Jeffrey—needs graciousness and thoughtfulness and courtesy and the outward signs of these things. The world is angry. People who never meant to become enemies could easily turn hostile. Think of Kathy and her father, for example, and the way he probably broods over what he takes to be her shallowness. And Kathy on her side thinks that her father doesn't know what it's all about and doesn't trouble to tell him.

If you and Kathy had been a little less lipsticked, a little less late-houred, a little less persistent of cigarette, a little deferential (as you should have been), he might have more hope today. How do you know that his impression of the modern girl will not affect his dealings with his own organization, his plans for the future? You should have given him something to work for.

They talk about destroying incentive a good deal today, and they usually are talking about destroying the incentive to make money. I wish more people would remember, especially you young ones, that you are the real incentive. If you aren't worth the candle, why play the game?

I know you are worth it. So do other lucky parents. But I wish Kathy's father knew it too. I wish he understood his daughter, and you. When he comes up to visit her at college, try to do something about that. Turn the other ear.

Love,

MOTHER

XII

LOYALTY

XII

DEAR SUSAN: I have your letter in which you stand up for Rosalie Rogers in spite of what she's done. She's certainly going to need every friend she has. When she comes back here to live, after that dramatic elopement, she's going to find many a cold shoulder turned her way. If you fight her battles, you're going to lay yourself open for a great deal of criticism. Apparently you already have, for you write that Mark thinks that you should have nothing more to do with Rosalie.

His whole family is outraged by what has happened. To have Rosalie run away with the man who was going to marry Mark's sister isn't a thing to be forgiven or forgotten easily. You can't blame Mark for the way he feels, but I can understand too why you don't think that you can drop Rosalie completely, or cut her the way a great many people are going to do. You've known that girl so long that she really is a part of your life, and you probably understand better than anyone else her queer combination of lawlessness and generosity.

A day or two before the elopement, I met her on the street. I forgot to tell you this, but in the light of what happened later it may have been significant. She asked about you. She looked, as she always does in talking to older people, a trifle unsure and unsafe and about-to-run and then she suddenly said, "I'd like to hear from Susan. Will you give her my love?"

She spoke like an awkward child, instead

of the accomplished siren she's supposed to be. It rather touched me at the time and I imagine that she must have been thinking of what she was about to do and all the things that people would say. Heaven knows that they have been said with many italics. So you can guess what your telegram must have meant to her. She couldn't have had many messages like yours.

It is too bad that you and Mark should have disagreed so violently about it and I must say that your letter sounded stubborn. It's the first time that his loyalties have clashed with yours, and it seems to have brought out a good deal of vehemence and determination in both of you. Naturally he believes that you should see the situation as an insult to his sister and be as ready as he is to frown on the person who was responsible for the insult. I don't wonder that he resented your sending Rosalie a message to wish her happiness, when he was wishing her all the bad luck in the world.

I couldn't have sent her a message wishing her happiness. I don't think she deserves it and I doubt whether she gets it. She's married—or is it better to say stolen?—a charming, unstable boy who must be oversusceptible. You say that she's always cared for him. Maybe that's true, but she's certainly made herself very conspicuous with other young men. She's been a trial and a cross to everyone who knew her, and personally I've grown tired of hearing what was the last wild or careless thing she did. If I were going to take sides in this matter, my judgment would have to go right along with Mark's.

But she isn't my friend. She is yours, and that makes a difference. I can't help being glad that since she is your friend you are not willing to join the hue and cry of gossip and condemnation. The world needs all the loyalty it has, and it is a pity to throw even a little bit of it away. One of the rarest things to find among girls is genuine loyalty to one another through thick and thin. Men are much more apt to stand by one another. They'll admit faults in the men they know. But they'll say, "Yes, but he's a good fellow," or just, "He's a friend of mine," and that closes the discussion.

That was true last summer about the boy who was visiting Mark. You didn't like him. You thought he was vain and egotistical. But Mark felt very differently. He stopped arguing with you about the boy's merits. But he didn't give up his friendship with him. I am sure that he would have felt that was dishonorable just because a girl didn't like his friend, even if he himself was in love with the girl.

So there you are, face to face with one of the problems that you'll have to meet every now and then in marriage and even in an engagement. There are various ways in which it is met. I know women who deliberately destroy every friendship with men that their husbands have, unless they approve of the friendship. And very often they can't approve, because a man chooses a wife on a different basis than the one on which he chooses men friends, and congeniality all around isn't possible.

I hope that you'll never try to cut Mark off from his personal friends. Mark does admire a certain type of young fellow whom you don't like. He forgives egotism in men if they have genuine ability. I've noticed that in him and it's a good fault. You find it very hard to forgive egotism and boastfulness, and plenty of the men whom Mark will want to bring home to dinner will be uncongenial to you. But you must put up with that.

I'm not really forgetting Rosalie. I'm coming right back to her. Because, in the same way that you ought to allow Mark his own choice of friends, I think he ought to allow you your personal friendship with Rosalie. I think that if you handle it wisely he will not only stop objecting to it but, in the end, admire your loyalty, and trust you more for displaying it. Not that he will ever like Rosalie. She is the provocative and flirtatious sort of girl that he definitely doesn't like, and that you often find exciting.

If he's like most men—and he's pleasantly normal, that Mark of yours—he probably doesn't feel that a girl's friendships amount to much anyway. Haven't you ever heard two boys laugh when they hear girls begin to say disloyal things about each other? It's a scorn-

ful and unsurprised laugh. Boys don't really
expect girls to have the kind of friendships
that they themselves have with other boys,
honorable and tolerant and lasting. For that,
I fear, we must blame the young ladies who
so willingly and so often tear each other to
pieces.

I know how disturbed you are. You don't
want to quarrel seriously with Mark, and
yet you won't toss Rosalie into the discard.
I don't think the choice is necessary. Tell
Mark—and tell him pleasantly, with the chip
off your shoulder—that she is an old friend
and that you know she has qualities that are
lovable. Then I wouldn't say much more about
it. See Rosalie when it comes about naturally,
but don't make it a defiance of Mark. If you
can manage that with frankness and without
quarrelling, you will find that Mark will respect your loyalty.

[159]

What a long letter to tell you that I am proud of you for standing up for Rosalie, even if she is a lost cause. And who can be sure about that?

Love,

MOTHER

to them before you were born, when I was in college. I have been to many of them since.

There was radicalism among students when I was your age, plenty of it. But I know that the times are not parallel and I do not mean to insinuate that this is just a matter of milestones and that you are going through a passing phase of interest in radical thought which will lapse and die in you as you get older. It may and it may not be a temporary matter with you.

Personally I would be very impatient if you did not take an interest in such meetings as these. It is very hard for me to keep my tongue off some young friends of yours who think that the world is only their tennis court and their dance floor. If, when you first are aware of it, you were not angry because of social injustice I would think your powers of sympathy were sluggish and your imagina-

[163]

tion weak. I would be ashamed of you, if you were unaware of the pressing difficulties of the world.

There was trouble enough twenty years ago, even before the war. Working conditions were far worse than now. There was child labor, there were shocking wage schedules, fire-traps of factories, little protection for women. Much of that has been bettered. The world is really more conscientious than it used to be. But you have seen what I did not ever have to see, thousands of boys and girls of your own age, caught in an impasse of unemployment. You've seen relief lines and attempts to create work that were often worse than idleness. I know that when you are told, as of course you are, that a bad system has brought all this to pass and that the system must be destroyed, you would be less than natural if you did not find yourself deeply affected by the radical argument.

But on the other hand I would be a poor parent and a worse citizen if I did not remind you right now that the United States is your country and that it is your duty, in return for advantages and protections which it has given you for some twenty years, to offer it your first loyalty, and not to let that loyalty be shaken even in times of trouble. You have every right to criticize the operations of a republican government. But don't be traitorous or subversive in doing so. Look out for that. As long as your government exists, and you do not deny or refuse your citizenship, I don't think you have any right to give loyalty and devotion to another government. That is what many students are doing. Some of them, even on your campus, have spoken to me as if Russia were their own country, and of that plan of government as if it were the only one to which they felt loyally bound.

I know some communists, here and abroad.

I respect some of them very much. Their final opinion is not mine, but it was gravely arrived at. But I do not respect the communism of the Tertius Bowdens. That young man and his wife live on dividends. Old Mr. Bowden worked and still works hard for the money which supports them, and the capitalist system keeps the whole family going. Tertius Bowden and his wife have never earned an honest dollar. They could not stand up for a week under the stringent, laborious, serious life in Russia. But they go around spreading the story that Russia is the only country in the world worth living in and that the Soviet system is the only one that can survive. Deep in their minds they probably have a conviction that communism in the United States will never happen and so they can have the cake of their income and eat the excitement of their discontents.

I feel somewhat the same way about the participation of young students like yourself in labor troubles and communist meetings. If a group of young people from some famous men's or women's college begins to start a demonstration, it is always the name of the college that appears in the press, and often the names of the parents of the college sympathizers. This shows, it seems to me, that students can not act as independent citizens, that they must wait. While they are in college they are not free to express a public partisanship without dragging in the names of people and institutions which are supposed to have a nominal control over them, and making those institutions and people become identified with movements with which they are not in sympathy, or which they can conscientiously support.

I can fairly hear you ask me if that means

that I want you to waste four years of your life in inaction. Quickly I answer no. I certainly do not. I want you to put these years to the very greatest advantage. I want you to study economics and especially the various systems under which the world is presently governed. That is what education is. It is study, not politics. I object to having schools and universities used as recruiting stations for class war. That was not what they were founded for, nor why they were endowed, and you must remember that you are living on that educational endowment. It was money laid aside for study, not for propaganda, and it is a misappropriation of funds to use it for propaganda.

Of course there is no sense in trying to preserve the atmosphere of the scholarly cloister in a time of social and political earthquakes. I know that. You have to keep in touch. I would rather have you go to a radical play in New York than to a night club. But that isn't the only kind of play I want you to see. Nor do I want you to read proletarian and propagandist literature only. I want you to be prepared to be useful to your country when you come out of school, and I don't think that the way to be useful is to so narrow your mind when you are young that you never have room for more than one side of the inevitable social argument. Nor do I want you to pledge yourself too young to any party. I have always hated the way war tries to excite and play upon the sympathies of youth, and class war is no better than international war in this respect.

What I hope is that when you are on your own you will do everything you can to prevent class war, instead of fomenting it. In this country the proletarian struggle seems to me to be an artificial set-up. The lines of division among our population are not clear or definite. We have no peasantry, no aristocrats in spite of some pretensions and extravagances, and the working people, hard as their lives certainly are, are not down-trodden. No one dares to do any treading on them. They vote. We have a great many people out of work, far, far too many poor, but bitterness does not solve these problems. It hampers solution. I have always thought that even if a class war were started in this country, it wouldn't last long. Too many people wouldn't know what side they were on.

If you had even a twenty-year perspective on the social and economic situation, you would see how great the improvement has been in spite of hard times. There has been much progress. The system under which we live is full of faults, but we do seem to be weeding them out steadily. Of course weeds come again. The world takes a lot of gardening. But think of this for comfort. Each generation's liberalism stands upon the shoulders of that of the previous one.

There are two kinds of people who remain socially useful throughout their lives. One is the citizen who is reconciled to the imperfections of the world, but in a kindly and industrious way never stops doing all he can to lessen them. Your uncle Fred is like that. He doesn't say much, but his influence changes things, makes bad conditions better. The other useful sort of person is like Professor Harris at the university. He is always led by a belief in an ideal which he thinks can be realized. He will never stop trying to attain it, and his kind of pull on the world brings it forward. People have always called him a dreamer, but he's one of the most forceful men I know.

[171]

I want you to be one or the other kind of person. I shall never quarrel with the fact that your politics and philosophy may not be mine. But I do not want these things to happen to you: I do not want you to be duped by schemers; or to fall in bewilderment from high hope to pessimism; or to spread false ideas; or to become exhausted from attempting the impossible; or to promote hate.

That is why on this May Day I do not want your thoughts to turn to violence, or to contempt, or to anything else which lessens your love for your country. Begin with that, never lay it aside, and you can go safely and usefully to as many meetings as you like.

Love,

MOTHER

XIV

MENTAL SECURITY

XIV

DEAR SUSAN: Your last letter sounded as if you thought the end of the world had come. I have looked carefully in the almanac and can't see that it has. What a dreadfully dreary conversation you and Mark must have had!

He has obviously had an attack of the fear which is epidemic among young men and women everywhere. I don't blame any of you for catching it. You have been exposed to constant complaint about the world and to all the nervous depression of your elders. So when Mark says to you that he doesn't know whether he can give you security or not, you both begin to worry and eye the future as if it were an ambush.

You ask me how I thought security could be insured, or words to that effect. I must say, and quite cheerfully too, that I don't think financial security can be made absolutely fast. There's never been a safety deposit box that could hide it away. Does that sound very unsympathetic? It isn't.

Think of the example of the Wilder family. They thought they were safe and provided for, no matter what happened. They had taken every precaution so that they would have financial security. But new laws were made, the depression lasted, and the Wilders are now hunted by fears. It is true that their resources have shrunk, but what has really undermined their security is not loss of money but the fact that neither of the children was

[175]

brought up to be resourceful or self-sufficient. The girl has come home to live and to fret, and the boy and his father spend their days trying to save fragments of their fortune. All day long they quarrel with the world, and it's the only world they'll ever live in.

In your letter you wrote that you thought we ought to make the government do something so that everyone could have absolute security. But the government can't do that. A limited amount of financial assurance can be promised and written into legislation to meet various problems of old age, and unemployment. So it should be. It will be effective as long as the government can pay its bills, which I trust will be forever. But even with the best that the government can do, and with its greatest solvency, the insecurity in the world will not be destroyed. I believe in old-age pensions and in unemployment insurance and in a well-managed dole, when we need one. This period of trial and error which we are going through will bring us some of these things and we'll gradually improve upon our methods of managing them. But security is beyond the power of government to bestow. It can not give courage to individuals who lack it, and there is no security possible without courage. It can not give mental resources to those who should have them. The sense of insecurity in the individual must, in the long run, be destroyed by the individual himself. He can be helped, but it can't be done for him.

I saw Ella the other day, our old maid of all work. She is very poor. She does a little cleaning in return for room rent and she has hopes of an old-age pension. She isn't very strong. But she cheered me immensely. She's always enjoyed living and she enjoys it now.

She has stored up thoughts and reminiscences and never becomes greedy and, as she says, she "always has to laugh at something." She's really secure and without any income to help her. Let her be a lesson to you.

You and Mark are worrying about whether it is "safe" to marry before he has an assured income. You must decide on whether you have nerve enough to do it. As things are working out, you can not count on money of your own. You know that. Years ago your father and I took what we thought were all the proper precautions to leave you a little money, but these financial upsets have changed that outlook. Luckily there has been enough to educate you. Depending on how long I live—and I'm still pretty active—there may be an inheritance for you.

But if there isn't, you can get along. Most of the people in the world manage without such helps. You are healthy and educated. Mark is learning a profession. Between you, you should be able to earn your way. But even supposing the worst, that you could not, you would not freeze or starve, in all likelihood. I have a great faith in the resources of this country and its generosity which makes me pretty sure that you wouldn't be allowed to starve. You might be humiliated and not very well fed, but so have been many others. You must face these chances.

It is your mental insecurity that I don't like, and I do blame myself for that. Is it because you've heard so much talk about money here and there and because all parents shake their heads and talk about how bad things are? Young, healthy people shouldn't be frightened even in adversity. When you get a little scared, I wish you'd do this: Think of those young women who set out across the United

States in covered wagons, as your father's grandmother did. What security did she and her husband have? Yet hunger and cold and illness were the same then as now, without so many public institutions to take refuge in. Those two had a couple of feather beds and that lovely maple highboy that is in your room today, and she had some unbleached muslin underwear, and a Bible, and that was about all. She didn't have a notion of what she would meet or endure. My own grandmother used to have Indians come to her door. Mostly they were friendly, but there was one time, when your great-grandfather was in the Civil War, that she had to run through the dark night to the next settlement to escape an Indian uprising and massacre. There weren't any relief agencies to take care of her, nor telephones; nor policemen; nor firemen. Yet do you remember that picture of her, taken after that period? She looked young in her late thirties, and competent and happy. And they didn't touch up photographs much in those days.

She didn't even have much financial security. Later they lost everything in 1893. She had mental security. Of course she always felt that she had God right with her, above the nearest, lightest clouds, taking personal interest in her fate. I wish you could feel that way. I wish all girls and all women could have that faith. But whether you can or not, try to get some of the kind of mental security she had. I'll tell you how I think it can be done, and this is a personal and not a federal job. There is no order in these recommendations. Follow them as seems best.

Establish a reasonable standard for your desires, first of all. Don't want too much of anything, not of wealth nor even of happiness. If you have love, and I think you have, you already have the best a woman gets. Take care of it. Life is not happiness. It is a beautiful and exquisite balance between joy and pain.

The second thing to do is to keep yourself competent. Whether you have a job or not, try to have something which you can do better than other people. Keep on with your study at odd moments, even if you have to do the housework, even if Mark gets rich in the end. When you know you are expert or even competent, it gives you a handle to the world.

Then you must have nerve. I don't mean the hard tenseness, the I-am-ready-for-anything attitude, that lasts for a day or a week. I mean continuous courage that will see you through money trouble and sickness and disappointment and even sorrow. It is the habit that will never let you feel sorry for yourself.

And cultivate an ability to enjoy things.

There is usually something to laugh at or to interest a person even in an old newspaper. Enjoy things as you go along, today, not waiting for tomorrow. Learn to keep an eye out for color and to hear lovely sounds. There are so many. All your senses should be kept in use. Even in unhappy situations there is sometimes something humanly interesting, or something suddenly funny, and it is that which keeps us from fainting under a load.

Also try to be flexible. If the world can't be run your way, or in the way you were brought up to expect, maybe some other way is better. If you are ready to cooperate with change, if you can bend without breaking, you will be secure when emergencies come. Also you will keep your figure, as well as your good spirits, if you are flexible.

Mark may earn a good income, but that won't give you security. The government may give you a pension, but even then you aren't safe forever. What I want for you is a mental security which means that as long as you live you will never give up, always enjoy life from its banquets to its scraps, and have a brave peace in your soul. Security comes from the feeling that life is not an abandoned or accidental thing; that it is part of a plan; that even its problems and its pains are not senseless cruelty, and that personal life is part of a great, guarded creation.

This, I know, is not easy to believe. Little children take it for granted. In maturity or old age those who are fortunate come to have such faith. It is in the years between—your years—that you doubt and wonder most. Yet it is then when you must lay the foundations of mental security, when you must earn it.

You earn it for yourself but you never keep it entirely to yourself. It spreads to those you love, if you have it. The man whom you marry will try to keep you secure as best he can. Do the same for him.

And don't let anything frighten either of you.

Love,

MOTHER